JONATHAN SEGAL CHICKEN ...

On the same day that God made seagulls, he made pigeons, canaries, and even chickens. And the chickens begat and begat until finally Jonathan Segal Chicken was born. He was a special chicken. A far-out chicken. A rebel chicken. He wanted to fly. And he learned how. And how!

Jonathan began his travels with a trip to New York, as a good Jewish-American chicken ought to, but that was only the beginning. After rescuing his brethren from a fried chicken establishment, he decided he was ready for bigger things. Israel, maybe. It's more exciting than Miami Beach. The whole world is ahead of him. And heaven, too. An hilarious book, with illustrations to match.

Jonathan Segal Chicken

Sol Weinstein & Howard Albrecht

Illustrations by Buck Brown

 Arrow Books

Arrow Books Ltd
3 Fitzroy Square, London, W.1.

An imprint of the Hutchinson Group

London Melbourne Sydney Auckland
Wellington Johannesburg Cape Town
and agencies throughout the world

First published by Arrow Books Ltd 1973
© Sol Weinstein & Howard Albrecht 1973

Made and printed in Great Britain by
C. Nicholls & Company Ltd., The Philips
Park Press, Manchester.

ISBN 0 09 908300 0

CONTENTS

Book One

Dawn came in at 4:45 A.M. on the farm of Nathan and Jennie Berkowitz, a four-acre plot of hilly, shrubbed land near the great resort hotels of the Catskill Mountains of central New York State known to tourists all over the world as the Borscht Belt. John Cameron Timex Chicken, the farm's wakeup rooster, sighed, shook the drowsiness out of his head and hopped up on a fencepost to do his thing. He let go a staccato cock-a-doodle, climaxed with a piercing trailing *do-o-o-oo*! that woke up the thousands of birds quartered in rows of low, tin-roofed houses.

In truth, John Cameron had had it up to his wattles with that cockamamie cock-a-doodle-do routine and once in his impetuous early days had even tried to vary the pattern of his job by emitting a wild alien sock-it-doodle-do sound he had heard coming

11

from a portable radio in the barn. (And how bad could it have been? he thought; after all, it *was* from a dance called the Funky Chicken.) But the end result had been catastrophic. Panic-stricken by this sudden deviation from the norm, the hens had gone berserk, dashing about in insane fury, some laying a dozen eggs at a squeeze, some laying square eggs, while others had completely freaked out and laid cheese omelets.

So, with one black look from Farmer Berkowitz that had clearly said, *Another blast like that and you'll be dinner tonight,* John Cameron had gone back to tradition, realizing ruefully that change was not part of a chicken's existence.

As if to underscore his dour philosophy, there were the others of the flock roused into movement by his breakfast crow, pouring out of the henhouses in a tide of russet, white, yellow and speckled gray, jostling each other in a ravenous (more aptly, chickenous) race for the food being dispensed by Mr. Berkowitz, a short but muscular old-timer in a stained cardigan sweater, a floppy hat and the baggy pants from a dark suit which once he might have worn to a wedding but which obviously had not been in contact with a tailor's steam iron since the Eisenhower Administration. While he doled out the

John Cameron Timex Chicken,
the wakeup rooster.

13

repast, Mrs. Berkowitz, her omnipresent housedress covered by a full apron, crouched in the vacated henhouses to gather the eggs. The large white ovals would be set in a prominent place, the smaller whites next to them and the less desirable browns, as is so often the case in society, put in the back of the basket. And there was one she didn't know where to put, for one hen, laying to a different drummer, had produced one in plaid.

Yes, John Cameron Timex Chicken mused, there they were, doing what chickens had always done since the beginning of time, eating as much as they could as fast as they could, totally immersed in a squawking, flapping fight for existence.

Except one. In a nearby meadow, far apart from the others, stood a russet rooster, all sinews and bone, his stubby feathers working furiously in the breeze. He was Jonathan Segal Chicken and more than anything else in the world, he wanted to fly.

And for Jonathan Segal Chicken, flying did not mean that paltry poultry three-second airborne burst a chicken sometimes achieves either in rushing for its food or bolting in terror from a fox or a hawk. It meant *flying* flying, up in the sky flying, wild blue yonder flying, the kind he had seen birds one-tenth his size doing with arrogant ease, robins, blue-

Jonathan Segal Chicken,
he was determined to fly . . .

15

jays, finches . . . even a miniscule humming-bird. There's a bird who hums 'cause he can't even remember the words . . . and *he* flies, Jonathan thought bitterly.

So for the last ten days, while the others pursued their mundane chicken life, Jonathan had been busy from dawn to sundown, testing the wind currents, trying to catch them in his tail feathers, racing over the ground in preparation for takeoffs, time and time again enduring humiliation by bouncing off barns, ramming tree limbs and once crashing through a billboard, leaving the adorable child in the Crest toothpaste advertisement still with no cavities, but also with no head. Once in his zeal, he had charged out onto the New York Thruway, barely avoiding a passing Ford Thunderbird, whose hood ornament, also a bird, had taken one look at this puffing chicken and broken into hysterical laughter. Those nights he had straggled back to the coop, dragging his tail feathers, on his oft-bumped head an egg bigger than any his mother ever had laid.

But on the ninth day, something amazing had occurred. During a pellmell rush, he had caught a current, made a subtle tucking in of his legs and, oh miracle of miracles, had been able to ride it some 300 feet and effect a smooth landing.

16

. . . those first flights were lots of fun.

In that moment, fifty feet above the ground, looking down at trees instead of up, he had been suffused with the rapture he had dreamed about. He was flying. And also, because he had scraped the top of an elm, bleeding. But that was a piddling price to pay for such ecstasy.

In his excitement, when it was time to return to the barnyard, he did not walk across the meadow as was his usual practice, but flew, landing smack in the middle of the flock pecking at the supper grains, causing immediate fright, for they thought Warfield the chicken hawk, a lethal foe, had come on one of his bloody raids.

"Wait, wait!" he called to the plump little behinds disappearing under the hen houses. "It's me, Jonathan. What's the matter with you? You all chicken?"

His familiar voice brought them back into view, some boiling in anger (albeit boiling was a hazardous experience for a chicken) at the startling manner in which he had appeared, a few of the cockerels and pullets definitely in awe.

"Oy," lamented his mother, the rotund Bella Segal Chicken. "Why, Jonathan, why? Why must you fly around crazy like a person without a head? It's my fault," and she beat her ample breast as all mothers, feathered or

18

**Morris and Bella Segal Chicken
. . . and their crazy son.**

19

not, are prone to do. "He got those idiotic ideas from me. Why, oh, why did I line his nest with brochures from Eastern Airlines?"

"You're right, Bella," was the smug remark from Morris Segal Chicken, his father. "His craziness comes from your side of the family."

"What do you mean my side?" Bella beaked back, on the defensive.

"Your brother Sidney, the one who fell in love with the weather vane . . . on a Baptist Church yet. He wasn't out of his comb, right? Jonathan," and he turned to his son, "you've got to stop this flying business. If the Lord had wanted chickens to fly, He would have given us wings."

"And what are these?" Jonathan answered, flapping his feathery appendages and rising five feet off the ground. "Coathangers?"

"Again with the smart answers?" his father said with blatant irritation. "Go to your coop without your supper."

"Morris, don't say that. He's all stringy and emaciated. It's a shame for the neighbors. They'll think I don't make a meal for my own son."

So Jonathan went to sleep without supper, but Bella Segal Chicken later that night did steal in shortly after he closed his eyes to slip a few kernels into his beak.

"Son," she said sorrowfully, "give up this nonsense. Come down to earth. There's a whole life for you down here, plenty to do. You've got friends to play with, a whole farm to dig up and in the next coop Rose Nitzberg Chicken has a lovely pullet named Marilyn, a fine, sweet girl, a social worker. She works with Capons, helps them to readjust. Would that be so terrible if you got together?"

"You don't understand, Mom. Ever since I was an egg, things have been laid out for me. I appreciate what you and Pop have done for me, but I've discovered there's something bigger out there than just pecking around a barnyard. There's flight . . . freedom."

"All I know is the life I grew up in," Bella said, but by then, Jonathan was dozing, a smile on his beak, for in his dream he was soaring high in the clouds, even faster than the swallows for whose benefit he was holding up a sign: CAPISTRANO — THIS WAY. Giving him a final pat, she went back to her nest where three eggs awaited her warmth to help them hatch.

Even a mother's entreaties cannot stay a headstrong boy from his dreams and the next morning and the next and the next and the next he was in the air perfecting his art, each hour discovering new ways to sharpen his skills . . . inside rolls, outside rolls, barrel rolls, even onion rolls, which he obtained by swooping down on Grossinger's, for a chicken still has to eat.

From that modest 50-foot level, he had vaulted ever upward . . . 100 feet, 500 feet, even to 1,000 feet where the air was colder, the winds wilder. With his increasing altitude came a corresponding increase in speed . . . 30 miles an hour . . . 40, 50, and he knew that by further straining, there was no limit to what he could achieve.

Flushed with triumph from his latest ventures in the sky, Jonathan again came fluttering down in the midst of the flock, an exultant "Geronimo!" issuing from his bill.

His childhood pal, Hennie Younghen Chicken, the acknowledged funny fellow of the flock, who because of the farm's proximity to those great Catskill hotels and their entertainers had picked up such humorous gems as, "Why does a chicken cross the road? To get a hen with a yen! Show me an all-chicken production of Shakespeare and I'll show you a fowl play!" greeted him with an amazed, "Wow, Jonathan, that's some finger-lickin' flight!" a remark which drew dark mutterings, for a term like "finger-lickin'" in a chicken's frame of reference was strictly hard-core pornography. "Fowl-mouth," one hen said heatedly.

Morris and Bella Segal cringed, for advancing into the center of the excited flock came a group of elders led by Tevyeh Mostel Chicken, huge, portly, a trifle gray around the wattles and wise in the ways of chicken-dom.

"Jonathan Segal Chicken."

The voice boomed out of the massive chest, and all in the flock quaked. One quacked, a duck in drag.

"Jonathan Segal Chicken," Tevyeh repeated. "You must stop this reckless, undignified flying. You are giving all chickens a bad name."

"But it's not that way at all," Jonathan protested, and the others shuddered. Here was an uppity young cock who had the temerity to question Tevyeh. "It means a new deal for chickens, a new lifestyle, a new reason for being."

"You are violating everything we stand for."

"But what is it we stand for? The highest we can get in life is to maybe stand on a roof."

Tevyeh smiled tolerantly. "A chicken on the roof. Sounds crazy, doesn't it? But in this Berkowitz barnyard, we're all chickens on the roof, trying to scratch out an existence. And what keeps us going, Jonathan? I'll tell you in one word. Tradition."

With that sacred word, the other chickens gathered in an immense circle, awaiting the next sagacious remark from old Tevyeh.

"It's *tradition*," and he made it sound scriptural, "that tells us chickens who we are, why we're here, what we must eat and who must eat us. Tradition even spells out what we look like. Now you may ask, Jonathan, why do I go around with this red comb on my head and these wattles and hackles under my chin? And I will tell you. I don't know. But it's . . . tradition."

Even as he intoned these words, they seemed to imbue all the others with his ancient fervor, the chickens began a sort of high-stepping Hassidic strut, the circle started to move, the roosters chanting "Yaidel, dai-del, dai," the biddies picking it up with their "biddy-biddy-bim-bime!" Tevyeh cleared his throat and sang.

"Who is the creature
Made for men to bite,
Every Friday night,
By the Sabbath light?
Whose awful fate is to end up on a
plate,

24

**Tevyeh Mostel Chicken,
leading the traditional dance.**

And feed the human race's face?"
The chorus cried out:
>"The chicken!"
>"Tradition!"

Tevyeh repeated:
>"The chicken!"
The chorus responded:
>"The chicken!"
>"Tradition!"

A group of hens came forth, proper and demure, yet eager to add their musical philosophy.

>"Who must know the way to sit upon an egg?"
>"A Grade 'A' egg?"
>"A Kosher egg?"
>"Who must sit and listen to the young chicks squawk?"
>"So Poppa's free to be cock o' the walk?"
>"The he-e-e-e-e-nnnnns!"

The chorus cackled:
>"The chicken!"
>"Tradition!"

Now the pullets came forth and in their high feminine voices told of their part in the scheme of this feathered world, and the capons, even higher and more feminine of voice, did the same, and Hennie the clown, ever theatrical, sang something about chicks and ducks and geese having to scurry, and though the music was swelling to unimaginable power, Tevyeh still heard Hennie's faux pas and screamed, *"Gevaldt!* Why are you singing from 'Oklahoma'?" and just stopped himself from dressing Hennie down, for "dressing" was another unspeakable obscenity in chicken talk.

As the music hit a crashing climax, all the dancers seemed to freeze in mid-squawk for old Tevyeh now dominated all, his feathers fanned out, his comb bobbing in rhythm and he said, "So you see, Jonathan Segal Chicken, without our traditions, our lives would be as perilous as . . . as . . . a chicken on the roof!"

Hennie Younghen Chicken snapped his claws. "Oh, man, that's dynamite! Tevyeh, why don't we take it to Broadway?"

"Enough of your show business nonsense!" the old leader growled. "Now you understand, Jonathan, that from egg to rotissimat, our life is predestined . . . " He bit his beak for, in his attempt to curb the excesses of this outlandish young cock, he had let slip another unspeakable obscenity — rotissimat. "Accept your life and live with us in harmony. We were not made to fly. Forget flying, landing, takeoffs."

"If I don't work on those takeoffs, I'll

end up in a restaurant as a take-*out*," Jonathan said, his bold comeback shocking the
circle, for who had ever dared to challenge
Tevyeh before? "And what I have learned, I
can impart to you," he went on, but by now
the flock, seeming almost to wither under
Tevyeh's baleful stare, was backing off, their
minds shut to his eagerness.

"I knew he was a troublemaker,"
sniffed Henry Cabot Chicken, a patrician
Plymouth Rock and the WASP-ish leader of
his white-feathered branch of the flock.
"Those kind always are."

And so, one by one, even Hennie, they
stole away and Jonathan Segal Chicken, who
wanted to fly, was alone.

Cut loose from the rest, he now experi-
enced complete solitude, but strangely did
not mind for, having crossed the line, he felt
free to follow his dream. He flew every wak-
ing moment, higher, faster, using the winds
as his rudders and propellants and was able to
circle over the entire Borscht Belt in one hour
. . . over Brown's Hotel in Loch Sheldrake
(Jerry Lewis's favorite hotel, according to
the New York Post) . . . over the fabled Con-
cord Hotel, where one night he swooped in
low near the nightclub and heard Alan King
attacking the American Medical Association,
an insurance company and three airlines . . .

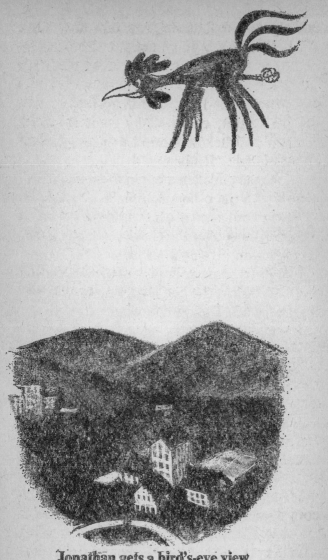

Jonathan gets a bird's-eye view
of the Borscht Belt.

over the bungalow colonies where he heard young comics with names like Arnie Bernie, Jackie Joey and Shecky Shtickey, all doing Alan King's act . . . over Homowack Lodge and Tamarack Lodge, with their grand old Indian names, operated by such grand old Indians as Blickstein and Levinson.

At night, feather-tired but happy, Jonathan Segal Chicken slept in the meadow, his break with the others complete.

But on one of those nights when a stillness hung over the Catskills, a night when Washington Irving's Headless Horseman might have come galloping over the hills crying out, "How the hell am I supposed to ride around when I can't see where I'm going?" he heard a rustle in the tall grass and saw two red pinpoints of eyes and a slavering mouth and sharp teeth illuminated by the moonlight, and he blanched for he knew that one of chickendom's most feared enemies was on the loose . . . a fox!

In nights past, he would have cowered in a corner under Bella's warm body, making ready for the worst, but the new, suddenly emboldened Jonathan was able to elevate in one burst some ten feet above the crawling marauder.

At the sight of the chicken hovering over him, the bewildered fox's long red bushy tail stood up in horror and he dodged as Jonathan dived at him, his spurs raking and beak pecking. *"Gottenu!"* screamed the fox. "It's impossible! I'm being attacked by a chicken. I heard of a worm turning, but never a chicken."

"Did you say *'Gottenu?'* — 'my God'?" said Jonathan, as he sat on a tree branch out of the fox's reach.

"Yes," said the fox. "And why not? My name is I. J. Fox."

"The furrier?"

"No, the fur. But you understand my language. Are you Jewish, too?"

"Vu den? (What else?) When your name is Jonathan Segal Chicken, you're not exactly a member of the New York Athletic Club."

"Ah," moaned the fox. "That's the trouble with the world . . . a Fox and a Segal, two Jews fighting each other for a living. Well, good luck to you, Jonathan, and I sure hope I don't meet any more chickens like you . . ."

"So long, I. J.," Jonathan said, but the fox was not listening, for he had already spotted a movement in a thicket and was hot after a Bob-White.

"Well," I. J. called back between chomps of the fowl in his jaws, "with a name like Bob White, he's fair game."

The next morning, Jonathan skipped his usual early flight for, during a restless night, he had made a great decision and now he was getting himself ready, cleaning off his fluff, taking a bath in a rushing brook and gobbling — uh . . . wolfing — uh, chickening down all the stray grains of corn he could find to give him nourishment for what lay ahead.

"Jonathan?" His mother's voice cackled softly in the dawn air. "You're leaving, aren't you?"

Jonathan looked down at his claws. "How did you know? I only made up my mind last night."

"A mother knows, Jonathan. I know there's nothing I can say that will stop you, but I just wanted to wish you Godspeed. And if God didn't give you such speed, you'd still be here with me, but that's another story," she said in sorrow.

"How's Pop taking my banishment?"

"Don't ask. But since you asked, I'll tell you. Morris Segal Chicken told me, 'Bella, we don't have a son anymore. Our son is dead. I'm sitting Shiva for him.' But this morning," and her voice lowered, "when I told him I was coming to see you off, that father of yours dissolved right in front of me like a blob of chicken fat. And he told me to give you this, because he knows there'll be days when you'll be hungry." She pressed something into his toes.

"Aw, Mom, you shouldn't have — a six-pack of worms."

"We were saving it for our old age, but you take it, son. Now, Jonathan, you'll take care of yourself?"

"I will."

"You'll keep your feathers dry. You don't want to catch a cold."

"I won't."

"And Jonathan, now that you're flying, you'll be meeting a lot of different things up there in the air. Like maybe a model airplane. They look cute, but stay away from them. Believe me, those mixed marriages never work. You heard about my brother Sidney with the weathervane."

"I'll stay clear."

"And, Jonathan," she seemed a trifle embarrassed. "I know you're part of a wild, new generation that does strange things, but you won't eat any funny seeds . . ."

"No funny seeds."

With a final clucking sob, she embraced him and rushed away.

The last tie cut, Jonathan Segal Chicken revved up his feathers, took a long run over the gentle grass, caught a felicitous breeze and was airborne, turning back once to look at the Catskills that had been his home from the moment he had been just an eggdrop in his father's eye, to see again old Farmer Berkowitz rocking on the front porch and sipping tea through a lump of sugar clenched in his bridge, to smell, possibly for the last time, that homey vapor of schmaltz herring that hung over Sullivan County's hundreds of hotels like a weather inversion, to see chubby ladies on the front lawns doing morning calisthenics between bites of chocolate eclairs, to hear a dozen loudspeakers cry out, "Complimentary dance lessons at 3 P.M. today on the handball court, featuring instructors Ricardo and Lucille . . . " Then he banked sharply and was gone to a new part of his life.

Book Two

"We gotta do something," said Saul Ilson, a bleary-eyed air traffic controller at New York City's immense John F. Kennedy Airport, to a fellow skywatcher. "I keep telling the FAA we're overworked monitoring hundreds of flights in and out of here every day, but they don't believe us. Dammit, they'd better believe us now because I think I'm whacking out; my number four engine just blew. Tell me, Ernie, is that thing you see on the screen a Cessna, a Piper Cub . . . or a chicken?"

Ernie Chambers giggled. His compadre in the tower had surely blown not only his engine, but his landing lights. "A chicken on radar?" He looked. The fat Corona cigar fell out of his mouth and singed his beard. "Saul, you're right. We'd better strike for shorter hours. I do see a chicken."

Jonathan Segal Chicken had come to the big town.

Though exhausted by his 100-mile flight from the farm (and awed, too, since this was the longest he had ever gone non-stop), Jonathan found he was too stimulated to even consider grabbing a cat, uh, chicken nap. What a wondrous sight unfolded before his eyes as he sat atop the railing on the 86th floor of the Empire State Building.

The town was alive with honking cabs, people scurrying in and out of subways, buses chugging down the main streets, stores ablaze with light, skyscrapers humming with activity . . . a certain electricity in the air about all of it, for which Con Edison was getting a pretty penny. Amid the hustle and bustle, he could see beautiful Central Park, an oasis of greenery, and its young lovers, who were mugging the old lovers. Riding on Fifth Avenue in an open car was the tall, photogenic mayor of New York, waving to the throngs and crying, "I'm handsome! I'm handsome!" At the entrance to Radio City Music Hall were two dozen lovely young ladies, the Rockettes, who in perfect choreographic precision were kicking a masher to death. In the harbor stood the lady with the torch, the Statue of Liberty, proclaiming her immortal message, "Give me your tired, your poor, your huddled masses . . ." Outside a 28th Street Welfare Office there was, indeed, a long snaking line of tired, poor, huddled masses.

"Holy Madonna," cooed a voice in his ear. It came from a disheveled, soot-covered bird that had flown onto the railing next to him. "I think I see a chicken. I gotta stop sipping from them Ripple Wine bottles on the Bowery."

"But I *am* a chicken," Jonathan said.

"Sure, sure, and I'm a Learjet just back from Acapulco where I threw a glittering soiree for Jackie and Ari and Liz and Richard at Merle's house. No kidding? You really a chicken?"

Jonathan nodded. "Yes, Jonathan Segal Chicken."

"Glad to see yuh, mac. I'm Pasquale Pigeon, from a long line of New York-bred and fed pigeons. How did you get up this high? Fall out of a plane?"

"I flew," said the proud Jonathan, and gave his winged companion a fast loop-the-loop in demonstration.

"Maron!" Pasquale's eyes popped. "What did they put in your mash — Vitamin E? Imagine that, a chicken that flies! Well, in the words of Plato, whom I often read, 'Ain't that a kick in the head!' What can I do for

you, Johnny, baby? You got what to eat, a place to sleep tonight?"

Jonathan gave his comb a negative shake.

"First thing, you come on down to the ground with old Patsy and I'll fix you up with a veritable Lucullan delight. That means," he said, while they descended, "a food freakout. This here New York is a gourmet paradise for birds. Anything you want is layin' on the street because, thank heaven, there are eight million slobs in the Naked City. We got it all . . . pieces of bagels, a slice of pizza, hot dogs with mustard, enchiladas, moo goo gai pan. In the space of one block, you could get heartburn in ten different languages."

They glided to rest on the coppery, weatherbeaten head of the statue of William Henry Seward, the secretary of state under Lincoln and the man whose purchase of Alaska from Russia had been sneered at as "Seward's Folly." Patsy, being a pigeon, did what pigeons normally do when they are in propinquity with a statue and Jonathan, not wishing to appear like a country rube, followed suit. "Oh, Lord," the statue moaned. "Seward's Folly wasn't Alaska; it was being erected here. I just got used to the pigeons and now the chickens are decorating me."

They pecked around a bit, snaring a pea-

Jonathan hits Broadway,
and meets Pasquale the Pigeon...

41

nut here, an ice cream cone fragment there and the other pigeons, also present for snacking, looked askance at Patsy's monstrous peckingmate, he of the red comb and the russet plummage. Not wishing to go into the whole explanation of how he happened to become a buddy to a flying chicken, Patsy told them it was his cousin, the actor, Walter Pigeon. "That's how they dress in Hollywood."

Moving from item to item in this Safeway Supermarket of the sidewalk, Jonathan came upon the scent of something warm and roasted emanating from a greasy cardboard bucket, obviously just discarded by a pedestrian. He was about to take a bite in curiosity when Patsy purpled and shoved a wing in his face.

"No, no! You don't want that, Jonathan," and the pigeon's eyes dropped in shame. "That's from a place called . . . " and he stammered, "Colonel Kentucky's Chicken Pickin's."

"*Gottenu!*" exclaimed Jonathan. "You mean . . . "

"Yeah," said a somber Patsy. "And they deliver. In the words of Kurt Vonnegut, whom I often read, where chickens are concerned that place is a *Slaughterhouse Five*."

A monstrous anger grew in Jonathan. He

knew from the teachings of Tevyeh and his parents that chickens were supposed to finish their earthly span on a Melmac plate some Friday night; that was preordained. But to be wiped out on an assembly line basis, that was hideous. Having nothing to gnash, because roosters' teeth were as scarce as hens' teeth, he dug his beak violently into the cement. But his anger fled with the boisterous, whirring arrival of a small brownish-gray English sparrow, humming "I've Got A Lovely Bunch O' Coconuts" and doing a music hall-type soft-claw dance on the statue's head. Recognizing Patsy, he chirped, "'Ow are you, you bloody Eye-tye? And 'oo's your ruddy mate here? Blimey, 'e's a fat one, like Peter Ustinov with feathers. Queer duck."

"Chicken," snapped Jonathan, "and who might you be?"

"Alfie's me name . . . gettin' through life is me game."

"What's it all about, Alfie?" said Jonathan, hating himself for falling into Hennie Younghen Chicken's joke rhythm.

"One more line like that and I'll give you a kick in your Bacharach," Alfie snipped back, proving he was no slouch at hastily improvised repartee himself and instantly winning Jonathan's admiration. This little cocky Cockney of an English sparrow seemed to be brimming with a kind of fun and verve not present in the flock he had quit.

"Not only is Jonathan a chicken, but he flies," said Patsy.

"Cor!" said a stunned Alfie. "I don't believe it."

In answer, Jonathan tensed, did a breakaway rush across the park that set Alfie to giggling, but then the sparrow boggled for this ungainly chicken was in flight, soaring higher and higher, and then Alfie and Patsy joined him and the trio flew a tight wing-to-wing formation over the Hudson River and through the canyons of Wall Street, in some instances ducking big buildings, in others the plummeting bodies of speculators jumping from big buildings. "I guess the market is down today," Patsy commented offhandedly.

And for Jonathan, this was a titillating experience. Never before had he flown with other birds and soon by watching the way Patsy arched his back and Alfie's curving of wings, he was duplicating their aerial maneuvers and picking up speed. Now he was certain he had chosen the right course, for here he was in a big city with two newfound buddies and he was flying the time of his life.

"Hey, *goombah*," Patsy puffed, somewhat abashed, for this eager-beaver chicken was now outdoing him. "Don't try to do it all

. . . and another Manhattan high-flyer,
Alfie, the English sparrow.

in one day. Let's relax a little. There's a groovy new spot down in the Village.''

Greenwich Village this night held the usual collection of exotic citizens, for which it has justifiably become famous, as was quickly apparent to the trio aviating over the 8th Street and Sixth Avenue intersection, the zonked-out corner of the world, where a hash house had nothing whatsoever to do with ham and eggs. The far-out types were on its corners pushing their varied brands of philosophy. On one, a bearded fanatic in a toga and sandals carried a sign, BECAUSE OF MAN'S BASE SEXUAL NATURE, THE WORLD WILL COME TO AN END IN FIVE SECONDS. He screwed his eyes shut, began his Doomsday-minus five countdown and when nothing happened, threw away the sign and leaped on a passing maiden. A Hindu mystic who served slices of Hebrew National Salami between chants, thus gaining the appellation "Swami Salami," leaned back upon his bed of sharp nails, and divested himself of an old proverb: "You can let love slip through your fingers, you can let money slip through your fingers, but if you let your fingers slip through your fingers, you're in trouble." A pothead, unable to make his connection, in desperation lit up one of his sideburns and smoked

46

it. He began to hallucinate at once and for the next twenty minutes had wild fantasies about dandruff.

"Same old Village," Patsy commented, but Jonathan, amazed at the thrumming scene, was discovering that life was more than just pecking for corn kernels. It was philosophy, argument, dialogue and especially culture. In front of a subway kiosk, a budding artist had set up his paintings in an outdoor display for sale to tourists. His works depicted a vast range of nonobjective themes — a Lockheed Tri-Star 1011 jet suckling its young, one hundred wavy lines entangled with each other which he had titled *One Hundred Wavy Lines Entangled With Each Other*, and a lone realistic piece, an elegant woman in a mink coat, holding a glass of wine and smiling a mysterious smile, which he called *The Mona Schewitz*, but none had aroused so much as a soupcon of interest. At that moment, Patsy felt a sudden urgency and, finding no comfort statue at hand, indecorously let it happen on one of the artist's blank canvases. Before the results had congealed, it was snapped up by a Teaneck, New Jersey matron, marveling at its depth of perception and boldness of execution. By the morrow it would be hanging over her fireplace to be ooohed and ahhhed at by the bridge club.

"Here's our waterhole," Alfie chirped, and the trio flew through the window of an abandoned, condemned building on Bleecker Street and into an ambience of lights, music and chatter. "This used to be a discotheque for people called 'Turn-On,'" Patsy explained, "but you know how short-lived these joints are. Since the jetsetters abandoned it, it's strictly for us."

And so it was, jammed with twittering, colorfully plumed fowl of many species, tapping their claws to the insistent rhythm of an all-owl rock band, *The Whooooo*.

"Welcome to the 'Playbird Club,' gentlemen," trilled a slinky redbreasted waitress. "I'm your Birdie, Robin. Are you all of legal age?"

They said yes, and she responded, "Good, we don't let Mynahs in here. What'll it be?"

Pasquale ordered a glass of gravel on the rocks, Alfie a caterpillar straight, with a moth chaser and both advised Jonathan to try the *specialite de maison*, Hartz Mountain Madness, bird seed imported from the Canary Islands. "It's organic," Patsy said.

From an adjacent booth erupted a heated argument about baseball and the respective merits of Bob Gibson and Dave McNally and

**At the Playbird Club Jonathan turns on
to lovely Robin Redbreast.**

Jonathan saw a cardinal from St. Louis going at it with a Baltimore Oriole. The floor was jammed with couples dancing beak to beak, ignoring the angry house poet, Edgar Allan Raven, who kept croaking, "Nevermore, nevermore."

"That's the only word the blighter knows," Alfie said in disgust. "Made a bloody fortune with it."

"Oooooooh." The suggestive sigh came from the throat of a gaudy lark in dyed blonde plumage, a lavender bill and eye shadow, who leaned a limp wing against his side, casting eager eyes upon Jonathan. "Look at those shoulders, those manly wings, and I love your russet feathers and the way they pick up the devil-may-care gleam in your eyes."

"Watch it," Patsy muttered. "This is trouble."

"May I introduce myself?" said the intruder. "I am Sir Lance-a-Lark, bon vivant free spirit and hairdresser to the birds. What's your name, big fellow?"

"Jonathan Segal Chicken," was the wary answer.

"From the size of that divine body, you're certainly no Chicken Little. I'd say Turkey Lurkey off the top of my head. Why don't you stop by my salon and let me back-

A look at the gay life,
and Sir Lance-a-Lark.

comb your comb? Oh, I can do wondrous things for you, you will just go ape—if our kind can do that.''

"What do you do in your salon?''

"Just everything,'' sighed the lark. "I check the peck, I tweak the beak, I burp the chirp, I thrill the bill and give you a ring-a-ding wing. Then later, we can fly over to my place, share a bottle of Cold Duck and look at my collection of Audubon etchings. 'Fess up, big chick, haven't you ever wanted to,'' the eyes gave a salacious wink, "go out on a lark?''

"Amscray,'' Patsy said in pigeon Latin. "Ever since Gay Bird Lib started, you've been impossible.''

"Oh, no,'' Jonathan cut in quickly. "Stay as long as you wish, Sir Lance-a-Lark. I can't go along with your particular needs, but being that I found a new freedom by flying, so should you fly in your own way.''

To Jonathan's surprise, the lark began to weep, the eye shadow trickling down onto the blonde breast. "Oh, if all birds felt like that, we'd be able to come out of the closet — or cage.'' He pulled himself up with a sort of sad hauteur and said, "Well, if there's no action here, I'm going home, turn on my TV and groove on the NBC peacock.''

The long day had taken its toll on Jonathan and neither the lights nor *The Whooooo* nor a passing lady fowl of the evening, who approached him and in a silken chirp said, "How's about it, handsome? For a hundred seeds, you can find out who the Bluebird of Happiness really is," could keep his eyelids from drooping. Patsy noticed and nudged him toward the window. Alfie said goodnight over Sullivan Street, hinting of an after-hour liaison. "Married," he smiled, "so we have to have a little back perch affair. But it's worth it. She's a parakeet and has she got a para keets! See you tomorrow, gents."

Patsy's mother, Teresa Pigeon, was an old world matron, stout and set in her ways, her neat black feathers tucked into a tight bun, a stylish gold spot on her beak, possibly the same outfit she had worn on the long trip from Sicily. She was a widow, she explained, whose husband, Dominick, a hard working carrier pigeon, had gone beyond the bounds of normal duty by attempting to carry the entire Sunday New York Times by himself. "And he might have done it, too, but that was the week B. Altman, Lord & Taylor and Bloomingdale's all carried white-sale supplements in the paper. The extra sections did it," she said morosely. "They percaled him to death."

A friendly sort, she did not let her

amazement at this flying chicken stand in the way of her usual hospitality. "So you fly," she said philosophically. "Why not? If creatures can ride around in automobiles, anything is possible, even a flying chicken. It's a new world, a free country and everybody can do what they want, regardless of race, creed or breed."

She found a soft spot in the coop atop the Sullivan Avenue tenement, flapped it clean with a few vigorous wing broomings, spread out some sheets of *Il Progresso,* the Italian newspaper, "in case you have to get up at night," and let him be. Ever restless, Patsy flew down to the street outside an all-night cafeteria to pick a piece of Danish crumb and Jonathan Segal Chicken was alone on the rooftop with his thoughts. It had been a monumental event that had brought him to New York, still twinkling with lights, even at this hour. He had learned much in this one action-packed day and he thought, why can't the others become flyers, not fryers, so they can see all this? Perhaps, the Lord willing, he, Jonathan, could be the instrument of a new salvation for his kind. Perhaps . . . but he fell asleep.

The rat-tat-tat flapping of hundreds of wings awoke him and before he even thought of food, his mind was on flying. There were

Jonathan on a speed trial,
over the Verrazzano Bridge.

Patsy and his flock in flight and Jonathan was airborne in a flash of russet, easily springing up to their level and then beyond. Their derisive cries were smothered by the subsequent *ahhhs* of envy. *"Maron,"* Patsy enthused, "you're getting faster every day, kinda like a logarithmic progression, in the words of Einstein, whom I read frequently."

While they sped over the Verrazzano Bridge ("that's a Sicilian span . . . one for my people") Patsy asked, "Jonathan, where did you get this knowhow?"

Jonathan, in the midst of an elegant maneuver in which he formed a figure-8, (the hard way — two 4's) called out, "It's all a matter of desire, Patsy. In fact, I had a dream last night. A Voice which may have been that of the Great Chicken . . . "

"Wait a minute," Patsy interrupted. "You mean God . . . "

"Sure," Jonathan asserted, now in a dazzling dive that caused the first chicken sonic boom, "God comes to every species. With us, it's the Great Chicken, with you, the Peerless Pigeon, with sea crawlers, the Big Deal Eel, and you, of all people, who are so well read, should know that even those pesky insects that buzz around a barn have their heavenly manifestation."

"That's right. I never thought of that —

the Lord of the Flies. But tell me," and keen interest appeared on the pigeon's face, "what did The Voice say?"

"It said to me, *'Jonathan Segal Chicken, any one of God's creatures can be more than they were born to be if they have the faith and the will to push on to new horizons.'* "

"Is that what The Voice said?"

"It also said something about staying away from Teflon pans at all times."

"Hey" panted Patsy, now not even trying to duplicate Jonathan's straightaway speed, "that's very heavy philosophy. You mean it's not just a fable? Like a frog could become a handsome prince?"

"If he tries."

"And a turtle could run as fast as a hare?"

"If he tries."

"Well," Patsy said, pointing his wing at a flock of gulls hovering above a garbage scow, picking their breakfast off the deck, "and how about the lowly seagull? Could it break its mold, get away from its limited world and go flashing at supersonic speeds into other dimensions and spheres?"

"I don't think it works for seagulls, but two out of three ain't bad," joshed Jonathan and signalled for Patsy to head for the 110th

Street rendezvous they'd set up with Alfie.

"Gents," said a red-eyed Alfie, just barely able to cling to a branch, his feathers mussed, a scratch along his back, "I ran into a spot o' rotten luck last night. 'Er blinkin' husband came home and I just about got away with me life, I did. He sicked a bloody cat on me, imagine that!"

They soon forgot Alfie's grousing (no mean feat for a sparrow) when they heard the bongo drums as they glided into the *barrio* of East Harlem. Here the hot spicy smells of rice and beans and baked plantains arose to meet their noses.

Pasquale and Alfie, seasoned tourists in this colorful section, angled down. "Come on, Jonathan. Try these. They're groovy." From under a vendor's cart, they scooped up the leavings of some delicacy or other and brought it to Jonathan.

It went into his tummy like lava down Vesuvius. "Oy," Jonathan grunted. "What is this that's burning out three square inches of intestines? I'll be a roast chicken from the *inside* out."

"Oh, that," said Patsy. "Just one of them choo choo fritos sprinkled with hot sauce."

But the frito-fired Jonathan was not even listening, just flying low over 117th and

Jonathan, Patsy and Alfie wing in
to East Harlem's barrio.

Madison, desperately questing for and blessedly discovering a half-nibbled Di-Gel tablet outside a *farmacia*. "Oy, what gas! If Israel had this much gas, the whole world wouldn't be fighting her, they'd be kissing her *tuchas*."

Di-Gel, living up to its claim, broke up the bubbles and he and the others flew on, but he tensed upon hearing the cackling of a tormented fowl and shot down to a backyard where two kids were flinging stones at another chicken, a great white fellow with a fiery red comb, easily twice Jonathan's size. For some reason, he seemed unable to move from a pile of rubble upon which he sat and thus was forced to take blow after blow. Two sharp pecks of Jonathan's beak sent Ramon and Estaban Sanchez away, howling, tears rolling down their cheeks.

"Hey, mon," said the grateful white chicken. "*Muchas Gracias.* You really somethin', *amigo.* You a chicken like me, but you flyin' . . ."

Jonathan tugged the trapped bird with all his might until he popped out of the rubble and then spotted the cause of his entrapment, two great, shiny, razor-sharp spurs at the back of his muscular legs which had become wedged between the bricks. Now liberated, he began strutting about the yard. He struck them against sections of cement, causing sparks to fly out.

"Say, those are wild shoes," said Jonathan, admiringly.

"These are my fighting spurs, *amigo*. I am Manolete Chicken, the greatest cock fighter in the whole *barrio*." To prove his boast, he slashed out with those fearful weapons and cut an enormous letter M into the red brick wall of the tenement. "Zorro, take your 'Z' and eat your heart out," he laughed.

Patsy and Alfie were circling cautiously above the flamboyant Manolete, but came down when Jonathan said, "They're friends."

"Hokay, any bird what's a friend of my *gringo* ees my fren'," Manolete spoke. "Come on, guys, I take you on the ten-centavo tour, but you gotta walk 'cause I don't fly."

The four birds . . . two chickens, a sparrow and a pigeon . . . started a leisurely stroll down 118th Street. In another neighborhood, this grouping might have caused a raised eyebrow or two, but here in the exotic heart of Spanish Harlem, no one seemed to notice or care, although one woman hanging out of a window did remark to someone sitting on the stoop, "*Caramba*, they're still coming in on the flight from San Juan and they seem to be getting shorter."

There was a bad moment when a cat, which had been scavenging in a garbage pail, looked up and licked its lips at the sight of hot lunch on the wing going by, but Manolete's eyes and spurs glinted in the sun and pussy backed off, muttering, "Senor, I don't mess with no cat with a blade, even when the cat ain't no cat."

Between bites of street food, Manolete talked of his dreams, a career in the Mexico City cockpits where he would fight epic battles in the sun, with blood on the sand, death in the afternoon and other colorful phrases, all coined by non-fighting Anglo-Saxons.

"Then I retire to a farm in Cuernavaca, where all I gotta do is *cu-ca-ru-ca-cu* in the morning and keep the hens happy at night. No problem for me, man; I'm *muy macho,* very manly," and he proved it by raking his steel blades and cutting a fire hydrant in half.

"That's *macho,*" Jonathan conceded.

It was at 125th Street when they noticed they had strayed from Manolete's bailiwick. The scraps in the gutters had changed from fritos and beans to ribs, collard greens, yams, and the tune, "There Is a Rose in Spanish Harlem," issuing from the loudspeakers over the doors to record shops was no longer the sadly sweet Santo and Johnny version, but the wailing, wild beat of Aretha Franklin.

At 125th St. they meet the swingin'
four and twenty blackbirds.

"Hey, *amigos,* I theenk I gone split. We in *Harlem* Harlem now." The great fighting cock waved a spur in farewell, promised Jonathan he'd somehow keep in touch and hopped on to the top of a down-town-bound cab, with a final flourish using his spurs to decapitate the OFF-DUTY sign.

At Jonathan's request, the trio shot up into the blue again and soared over the teeming corner of 125th Street and Seventh Avenue, for although he had spent a pleasant hour back on the ground, he was again desirous of flying.

"Hot damn! A chicken that flies!" The voice, sly and raucous, came out of an ebony fowl, sleek and shiny, who was perched on the roof of a tall building, surrounded by four and twenty blackbirds. "Come on down here, you muthuh. We wants to take a good look at you, you honkey chicken."

"Of course," Jonathan said politely and glided to the roof to extend a claw. Pasquale and Alfie came in behind him, inwardly sorry that the fearsome Manolete was no longer around to cock his intimidating spurs, for they had their tiffs in the past with this bunch.

"What you dudes doin' uptown on our turf?" the leader said, a grin on his beak but the hint of menace in his eyes.

"Just showing our pal, Jonathan Segal

Chicken, the town," Patsy said. "What's your name?"

"I am Eldridge Blackbird, author, lecturer, and feathered freedom fighter. Well, now, a flyin' chicken." He burst into peals of laughter. "Ain't that a riot?"

"Riot?" chirped one of his followers, Angela Blackbird. "Right on!" And before anyone knew what was what, that magic word sent the four and twenty blackbirds zooming down on a Kash 'n' Kredit furniture store where they smashed like projectiles through the windowpane and came out lugging a 19-inch Zenith TV set.

"Cool it," Eldridge said. "Why you-all bustin' yo' beaks? Ain't nothin' worth watchin' on that racist medium anyway. No brothers on the tube tonight. Redd Foxx ain't on, Cos' ain't on, Flip ain't on. Hell, man, this is white night."

"Why are you stealing things?" said Jonathan.

"They steals from us; we steals from them. It all evens out." Eldridge Blackbird sighed; this newcomer would have to be taught the ground rules. "We here is the underclass in the inner city of the ghetto and as such must ofttimes take unorthodox measures in order to insure our survival in a hostile environment. You dig?"

"Sometimes. Mostly, I scratch."

"No, chick, I mean . . . like . . . do you *dig?* Do you comprehend? Do you dig what I'm layin' down?"

"You lay?" Jonathan was wide-eyed. "You're a male. How can you lay eggs?"

"Oooooooweeee, we really got ourselves a nowhere square. I suggest that if you wish to dig my righteous, heavy message, you should pick up a copy of my book, 'Fowl On Ice,' which I'll be glad to peddle to you for 125 seeds or ten worms, depending on the kind of currency you carryin'. I do accept Bird Americard . . . or Masterchirp."

"But all you should be interested in is flying," said Jonathan, caught up in his zeal. "Flying means perfection, attainment, realization . . . "

"Those abstractions are groovy for you downtown dudes who got it all and, believe me, we gonna do all them things some day, but right now, we got to work on the basics, you dig? We want a sense of propriety in a free society . . . the real nitty-gritty in a decent city . . . "

Angela picked it up. "And a place on the ledge where we ain't on edge."

A third member, Stokely Blackbird, chimed in, "And jelly in the belly and a nest that is best."

Eldridge Blackbird lays it on,
a little rhetoric for Jonathan.

And suddenly, the four and twenty blackbirds were caught up in a soul-slapping, wing-flapping, down home rock and revival number so infectious that even Jonathan felt the need to sway, slap, and snap. And soon all were singing:

> "A place on the ledge where we ain't on edge,
> "And a four-door cage that's all the rage,
> "And jelly in the belly and a nest that is best,
> "And an all-weather feather when we get it all together . . . "

"Let's leave," Patsy whispered. "This is starting to sound like that all-bird rock festival, Woodcock, and it can go on all night." Thus, Jonathan and his cohorts bid adieu to the ecstatic blackbirds and flew back toward Sullivan Street.

Alfie begged off from any further touring. "I got a date tonight with a sweet, young thing. Told 'er I'd get 'er on the Ed Sullivan Show and make her a big starling."

"But Ed ain't on the air anymore," Patsy protested.

"Shhhh! If you don't say nothin' I won't say nothin'." That salacious gleam back in his eye, he doused himself in an exotic fragrance, Cage Rage No. 5, and was off for another round of love.

"How do you like that?" Patsy shook his head. "A horny sparrow." Since both were rather fatigued, they flew slowly back to Sullivan Street, letting a fortuitous breeze take them like two graceful sail planes, made one highly necessary pass at the statue of Seward, connected with driving layups that Jerry West and Walt Frazier would have envied and landed on the coop in the dusk.

And so the days passed into weeks, the weeks into months, the months back into days, for in this saga of a chicken who learned to fly, even time itself was altering its normal pattern. Jonathan continued to learn much of city life, its triumphs and tragedies, its ups and downs, and with knowledge came greater desire and with greater desire came greater efficiency in his daily flights.

On one day, using the Pan Am building heliport as a launch pad, Jonathan was able to actually outspeed a Sikorsky 'copter, causing the pilot to do a doubletake as the chicken made a mockery of his powerful rotors. That day he hit 300 miles an hour, then 350 the next and by the weekend, he had a very weak end . . . but the unheard of speed of 400 miles an hour.

Again at night, The Voice of the Great

Chicken came to him and now he knew not whether it was fantasy or reality, so intertwined had both elements become in his life. The Voice urged him on to greater and greater effort, more and more understanding and added "never turn your back on an 1847 Rogers Brothers fork."

"You know, Patsy," Jonathan remarked one evening, "I feel something within me is saying, go home and teach my brothers under the feather all that I have learned."

"Knock it off, Jonathan," Patsy said testily. "You were kicked out of the flock by this old Tevyeh guy, right? They turned their tails on you, right? Forget it. Stay here in New York. Here's where the action is. Or with the speed you got now, you can have a ball, fly to Florida in the winter, Canada in the summer, Europe, wherever. Just watch out for the Cook's Tour, that's all. But, otherwise, you could do anything you want."

Patsy's words were tempting, but Jonathan still remained troubled. Good life or no, there must have been a reason for this startling transformation. Why had he alone been singled out by the Great Chicken? And he knew the answer. He had to fly back.

"I'll never forget you and your mom, Patsy," said Jonathan, poised on the ledge to take off one clear Manhattan morning when

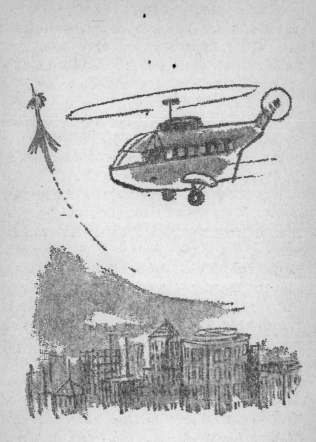

... and Jonathan's speed increases,
helicopters are but child's play.

the smog by mistake had taken a left turn and gone to New Jersey. "I wish I knew how to repay you, but anything I'd give you would be chicken feed."

"Just," and Patsy's cooing broke into a kind of pigeon sob, "keep in touch, huh?"

"I'll say something for you at the top of St. Patrick's this morning," said Teresa Pigeon, the tears swimming in her eyes as well. Even Alfie was morose. "I'll miss you, mytie," but then he smiled. "Here, if you're ever up in Maine," and he whispered the address of a nest in Kennebunk Port, "see Phyllis Finch. A proper New Englander and all that because she flies around libraries, but you connect with her out of moulting season and watch out! She's dynamite!"

Now he could contain his own tears no longer, so he kicked out, caught a brisk thermal, got his wings going and shot away, destination north.

The sky was blue and clear and empty and so he let it all out, zipping at a steady 400-mph pace.

It happened just a few minutes out of the city as he followed the Tappan Zee Bridge to Nyack. On Route 9-W, he saw the flashing sign that made him break speed and curve downward. It said COLONEL KENTUCKY'S CHICKEN-PICKIN'S and outside were hundreds of people milling about. Obviously, this was the gala opening day for the Colonel's latest franchise for, indeed, the reedy old Kentuckian himself stood on a platform addressing the spectators.

"Howwwwwwwwdeeeeeeeee!" squeaked Colonel Kentucky in his best Minnie Pearl style. "I surely hope you folks up here in Nyack are gonna be regular patrons of the colonel's fine old Southern-style fried chicken," and Jonathan felt his gorge rising, the image of that greasy bucket and its grisly contents in his mind. He headed down for a closer look and to his horror spotted in cages piled atop the flatbed of a huge truck hundreds and hundreds of his brethren awaiting their doom.

"Just wanted you-all to see these fine feathered friends in their live state, so you can be assured you're gettin' the best of the barnyard," the entrepreneur went on. "And here's a little kneeslapper for you. Why does a chicken cross the road? To get to the Colonel's ever-lovin' oven, that's why. Hee, hee," and he did, indeed, slap his knee and the crowd roared at his jocular cackling, the trademark of all his public appearances and TV commercials. "Yup, you're gonna love my birds, whether they're fried, fricasseed, broasted, roasted, boiled, broiled, or even my new novelty, a chicksicle, a chocolate-covered frozen chick on a stick."

Each of his words cut through Jonathan like a Flint carving knife . . . broasted, roasted, boiled, broiled . . . *Gottenu!* Never had he heard such a string of obscenities in his short life. Patently, the lanky man with the long frockcoat, the stringtie and the silvery beard was . . . Chicken Enemy Number One . . . and he, Jonathan, would have to do something drastic to stop this carnage. But what? What could one chicken do against this well-Wesson-oiled murder machine? Now he was on the ground, standing on the fringe of the crowd, wracking his brain for a solution.

So intense was the anger in his being, that he did not hear the footsteps padding behind him and suddenly ten meaty man-fingers encircled his feet, he was upside-down squawking and flapping his wings, but unable to move, and a voice laughed, "Say, Colonel, here's one that almost got away."

"Well, stick that critter in a cage with the rest. In a few minutes, he's gonna be a $1.49 special with biscuits, honey and buttered mashed potatoes to keep him company. Hee, hee . . . " and again came that hideous cackle.

And so it was that Jonathan Segal Chicken, the groundling who had learned to fly in order to achieve freedom and dignity, was imprisoned in a cage with his kin, about to meet his just dessert . . . but, unfortunately, he thought with bitterness, he wouldn't be just dessert, but the main course.

Book Three

"Idiot." The epithet came from a lovely dark-feathered pullet in the crowded cage, who identified herself as Ali MacClaw. "Why did you let yourself get caught?" she said in her theatrically trained voice. "There you were, free as a bird, to coin a phrase, and you fell into that Kentucky killer's clutches. Why didn't you just walk away from all this?"

"To begin with," Jonathan said, "I don't walk; I fly," and heard a few hoots from a handsome cockerel named Rich Littlechick, a fantastic impersonator who was able to reproduce owl sounds. "And secondly, I came here to help liberate you."

"Bananas," sighed Woody Allyn Chicken, a slender fellow with an unruly comb flopping about his head and circles under his eyes which gave the appearance of hornrimmed glasses. "Bananas. We have a chicken who's gone bananas. Probably resulting from a distorted childhood during which he was breastfed by an incubator."

The others laughed, but the sounds were mirthless and strained because they were all cognizant of the fact they soon would be heading for the Great Fork-Off.

"I really can save us," Jonathan said. "Just follow me when the time comes."

"Saved? Saved? What's all this talk about being saved?" said an old hen, Biddy Boop. "This is the day we've all dreaded since we cracked our shells."

"No it isn't," Jonathan retorted, and there was such authority in his cackle that somehow the others began to listen. "Do you all want to get out or take that esophageal slide to doom in a human's stomach?"

"But it's inevitable," Biddy Boop said in a tired voice. "That's why we've been fattened up all our lives."

Despite the overcrowding in the cage, Jonathan muscled his way into the midst of the bedraggled flock and spoke in a ringing tone:

"Do you want to get out?"

There was such a crackle in his cackle that it electrified the others and they began to bang against the bars and yell, "Yes, yes,

yes!"—suddenly realizing they had been lying to themselves all their lives. "Yes, yes, yes . . .!"

"Sure, sure, you guys in them white uniforms with the spatulas in your hands wanna take me down Death Row, but I'm breakin' out, you hear me?" It was Rich Littlechick slipping into his John Garfield-in-the-Big-house voice, then into Bogart. "I'm with you, sweetheart."

· "Play it again, Sam," Woody Allyn Chicken said and even he, cynic that he was, was now swept up by this fervor for freedom. "Fantastic, Jonathan. Count me in. Don't let my elfin size fool you 'cause under this scrawny body beats the strong heart of a pervert."

"The time is now," Jonathan said, for they were all being hoisted by sweaty, grunting humans into the rear of the new roadside stand where others stood ready to kill, pluck, and cook.

Colonel Kentucky was chuckling. "I reckon it's time to open shop. I mahself am gonna do the honors on that," and his beady eyes focused upon Jonathan, "brazen little feller we found running free outside." He reached his corded hand into the cage and grasped at Jonathan, but this was the moment the plucky, unwilling to be plucked Catskill cackler was waiting for. In the brief instant the sliding top of the cage was open, he flashed out like a russet rocket, soaring to the ceiling.

"Oh, my God, he *can* fly!" screamed Biddy Boop. "Go, Jonathan, save yourself! Fly out the back door!"

"That damn red chicken is pesky as a porcupine in a pea patch," snarled Colonel Kentucky. "I gonna take care o' him mahself." And reached for an axe.

But as the steel edge glinted on its way up, Jonathan was powerdiving on his way down, like a feathered Phantom Jet taking evasive action, easily dodging the cutting edge and landing a sharp beak flush on the seat of Colonel Kentucky's white linen trousers and the old tycoon yelped like a boy stung by a hornet. "Goldarnit," he whimpered. "He ain't no chicken! He's a damn devil!"

The "damn devil" whooshed around the Colonel again and again, landing penetrating painful pecks, causing the codger to jump up and down howling, with a graceful slash of his spurs copied from Manolete, he carved CHICKEN LIBERATION on the Colonel's bottom and, because there were so many letters, the slogan ended up on the backsides of three frightened countermen.

Jonathan makes a point with Col. Kentucky.

The rest of those in Jonathan's cage had broken out, inspired by the feathered bombardier inflicting his telling pecks on the Colonel and his men, and they, free for the first time in their lives, went for their tormentors in a savage cackling surge.

"Keep on truckin'!" Rich called out, biting an ankle. "No, keep on peckin'!" shrilled Ali MacClaw. Despite her slender physique, Ali was a formidable fighter, indeed.

"They've all gone mad!" screamed one of the men diving through the window, sending shards of glass flying. "The others!" Jonathan cried, "I must free the others!" He dove down at the stacked-up cages, bulled them over, and chickens by the score began to crash their way through the broken wooden bars.

One of the Colonel's men, being simultaneously pecked by Ali, Woody and Rich, screamed, "This never would have happened if I had been working at McDonald's. They've sold 12 billion burgers and not one of them ever ran amok."

Now the flood of chickens was scrambling over one another in a race to climb through the broken pane, chased by some of the whitecoated attendants who had regained their courage and also by a few customers who thought it was an opening day promotion. "Must be a lucky number in one of those chickens," one man reasoned.

When he saw they had reached the parking lot, Jonathan cried, "Now . . . fly, fly! Catch the wind and fly! You've got wings, use 'em!"

Alas, even freedom could not shake out of most of the scurrying flock their vestigial habits and, like the frightened fools they were, they could not or would not listen to Jonathan pleading, "Follow me . . . follow me . . . " And so, they met their fate, recaptured by the Colonel Kentucky crew or hit by cars, and saddest of all were the bewildered ones who almost immediately ran back into their cages for refuge and security and did indeed end up as $1.49 specials.

But a few did not. Rich and Woody and Ali followed in Jonathan's wake, at first managing only a few feet of flight as he had earlier. But with his constant urging and the adrenaline pumping in their glands, plus an occasional boost from their leader who flew around to their sagging tail assemblies and kicked them to greater heights, (even to nearby Yorktown Heights), they flew — badly, raggedly, out of formation, but they flew.

"Hey, this is super," said Rich. "It sure

was worth fighting for, this flying stuff." Woody poked his head into Jonathan's face. "Did you see me back there, Jonathan? Wasn't I fantastic, my beak pecking out combination bites like George Foreman working over a punching bag."

"Ali really surprised me," Jonathan smiled. "She was a regular Muhummad Ali. Tell me," and he turned to the pullet who churned the air with her delicate feathers, "where did you learn such violence?"

"From the great chicken filmmaker, Sam Peckinclaw," she revealed. "I had a bit part in a flick of his called 'The Wild Flock.' "

Woody's head spun. "Say 'movie.' Don't ever say 'flick' to a chicken."

In Jonathan's heart was sheer exaltation. He had taken three chickens aloft and they had made it! Next would come the hard, unending days of trial and error, early morning flights, night missions, all that goes into the shaping of a true bird on the wing.

He proved an apt teacher for, in a time frame even less than his, they were mastering those barrel rolls, loop the loops, power dives, learning to use the wind and tasting the delicious fleeciness of the marshmallow clouds.

Now he realized more than ever that he

Jonathan returns to the farm to
recruit with three friends.

must return to his home to teach the others for, if four could now fly, how many more had that potential lurking in their breasts and wings?

So, after two months of intensive, around-the-clock flying, Jonathan commanded his students to descend to a golden meadow ringed by great oak trees. They flew down smartly, wing-to-wing, and landed, awaiting his pleasure.

To their surprise, he flew over to one of the oaks, stripped off several leaves with his beak and flew back, placing several clusters on the wings of Rich, Woody and Ali. They stood straight and proud.

"You have learned well," said Jonathan softly. "These leaves signify that you have passed your course and are being graduated as instructors."

"How do you like that?" said Rich Littlechick, now in his John Wayne voice.

"We're chicken colonels!" Woody piped up, "I'm basically an antimilitaristic type, so I'd better get out of this chicken outfit."

"That's one thing," Jonathan said, pointing to Woody's feathers and beak, "you'll never be able to do." Then his face grew serious. "My friends, my job with you is complete."

"But, Jonathan," said Ali MacClaw,

"what are we going to do without you?"

"You don't need me anymore."

"But," Rich protested, "we may be good and all that, but there's so much more we can learn from you," a little Jimmy Stewart stammer creeping into his tone.

"I'm going back to my flock. I don't know how they'll take to me. After all, I left as an outcast. But you can come with me, if you're game."

"If we don't come with you," said Woody, "we're definitely game." And two gunshots punctuated his little joke for a red-capped hunter had fired at the standing foursome, but luckily, being a typical hunter, all he was able to hit was another hunter.

As one, the foursome took off and in a matter of a minute they had pierced the cold, bracing cumulus and were now riding above a white billowing sea at the astonishing clip of 535 mph, alone in their serenity and power.

But not alone for long.

"Hey, guys," Jonathan said. "Look, coming up aft of us." They all wheeled to catch the sun flashing coruscating showers on the fusilage of a great 747 jet plane whining along at the same rate.

It was while they were dipping their wings in salute to their monstrous mechanical brother that Jonathan spotted something dangerously awry. The rear door of the humpbacked leviathan was open.

And there, silhouetted in the doorway, was a rangy, crew-cutted man, a parachute pack on his back, a satchel in one hand, and in the other an Elizabeth Barrett Browning automatic rifle, set to spit its poetic message of death . . . *How can I kill you? Let me count the ways* . . .

Cowering, her hands behind her neck, was a trim, petite stewardess, under the gun and pale with fear. Her "Fly Me" sign had melted on her lapel.

And Jonathan Segal Chicken knew in a flash from newspapers Teresa Pigeon had set around the coop in New York that the man with the hard eyes and the determined face was none other than the most infamous of all skyjackers, D. B. Jumper! Obviously, Jumper, his satchel crammed with loot, was preparing a bailout over a designated spot where his confederates would pick him up.

Inside the plane, Jonathan could see total chaos. The pressure from the outside had driven the piano bar's Steinway fron first class into tourist and with it the pianist, bassist and drummer, a magician, two Playboy Bunnies and a pro football star still signing autographs on the run.

"I've got to do something," Jonathan

. . . and the four fearless flyers
encounter a highjacked 747!

91

said breathlessly.

"Cool it," said Woody. "Why should we get involved? You know what humans do to us. I say forget it and let's go on with the winning of the Catskills."

Rich Littlechick's typical response was to start whistling the theme from the "High and the Mighty," but Ali, ever intense, said, "Do what you must, but be careful."

Jonathan broke into a slanting pattern and wings down, eyes ahead, sailed through the doorway. Whack! He hit the skyjacker's midsection full force, sending the man to the floor and the Browning flying out of his hand. The stewardess quickly slammed and bolted the door, but Jumper was on his feet at once in a catlike recovery and crouched into a karate position. He sent two passengers spinning back with forehanded cuts and was just about to retrieve his rifle when Jonathan went into battle.

For thirty wild seconds, it was man against chicken, hand against claw, shoulder against wing, nose against beak, punch against peck, peck against punch, Punch against Judy . . .

During the melee, Jumper managed to grab Jonathan's neck for the death squeeze, but again the lessons he had learned from

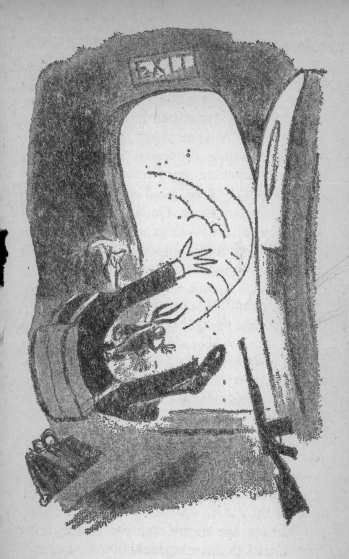

In a stratospheric melee, feathers fly
but Jonathan wins.

Manolete on in-fighting paid off and his scrabbling claws found naked skin and left five weals running from brow to chin and it was all over for the blubbering Jumper. Three stewardesses pushed him into a seat, asked him politely "Will you please fasten your seat belt?"' and then proceeded to knock him silly, not by unnecessary force, but with the secret weapon of all good airlines . . . five kinds of wine, three kinds of champagne, fruits, cheeses, Macadamia nuts until Jumper fell into a complete stupor. They had done their job, they had serviced him into unconsciousness.

Jonathan, meanwhile, his every little bone aching, dizzy because a few of those flailing blows had landed, flew limply around the plane, and crashed through a mid-aisle movie screen upon which a feature film was being shown. "My God!" a silver-blue-haired matron cried out. "Barbra Streisand has left Ryan O'Neal for a chicken!"

Round and round in tight loops flew Jonathan, his strength slowly returning, until he at last spun about and headed back to first-class. And there, on the serving cart being pushed by a stewardess, was a gigantic carcass of a chicken, and a chill sped through Jonathan, for he knew that only one bird in all of creation possessed such powerful thighs, legs and breasts . . .

It was Tevyeh Mostel Chicken.

An ironic twist of fate, indeed. Tevyeh, he who had been so steeped in tradition; he who said that chickens should not fly; he was flying 35,000 feet up, as high as Jonathan himself had ever flown.

At least, Jonathan thought, a sad smile wrinkling his beak, Tevyeh's going first class. He made his way back to the rear door and flapped his wings against it; a tall, buxom stewardess, seeming to sense his desire to leave, (and besides, he had no ticket and his presence would have to be explained to the agents with the bookkeeper mentalities on the ground; then they'd have to decide, does a chicken go full price? half-price? student standby?) finally figured the heck with it, opened it and let him fly free.

"Holy Lindbergh," said the flight lieutenant, striding out of the cockpit. "Have we just been saved by a chicken?"

"Yes," whispered the trim little stewardess whom Jonathan had liberated from D. B. Jumper. "And who was that chicken?" She looked off to see him fly away in a cloud of clouds. "I . . . I wanted to thank him."

Book Four

Dawn came in at 4:45 A.M. on the farm of Nathan and Jennie Berkowitz. And to herald it, up on a fencepost hopped Longines Leghorn Chicken, the farm's new wakeup rooster, for John Cameron Timex's time had run out long ago, as had the lives of Morris and Bella Chicken and so many others, for although Jonathan had not been gone long by man's standards, it was a whole generation for chickens. Longines let go a protracted crow, that same dreary old cock-a-doodle-do from time immemorial, that woke up thousands of birds quartered in low, tinroofed houses.

Among them was Hennie Younghen Chicken, once the funster of the flock, but who, because of attrition, was now its plump, pompous elder. No more would Hennie keep the others rocking with laughter. That was now undignified. He had hired a duck named Allan Drake to do the one-liners. Beside him was his wife, the once slim, attractive Marilyn Nitzberg Chicken, whose pullet days were over, for now she had scores of chicks of her own and, because she was the wife of the leader, was the president of Hendassah, the charitable organization of females, who cared for the old and indigent by taking to them little baskets of matzoh crumbs filched from the Berkowitzes' garbage for the Passover holidays. Unlike their human counterparts, they would never dream of taking chicken soup to the ill.

Aside from the change in leadership, everything was pretty much as it had always been, thousands of chickens pecking at kernels, squawking, arguing and carrying on their routine life. Except for one deviation; here, where he had first flown, the legend of Jonathan Segal Chicken was very much alive. The few who had witnessed his flight and were still around to whisper about it, had aroused a great curiosity, especially among the ever-restless young who nurtured the tale but dared not speak about it in the presence of the Establishment.

Hennie waddled into the midst of the flock for the daily briefing and the thousands stood still at attention. "Fellow chickens, here are some items on the morning report. First, I want to congratulate all the chickens from the 441st Laying Batallion for last night laying their one millionth egg. The Double EE pennant for Egg Excellence is being whipped up right now from a Simplicity Pattern by Mrs. Berkowitz and will soon be flying on your tin roof.

"Secondly, now available in Coop 37, our farm commissary, is that marvelous new chicken vitamin, Worm-a-Day, which contains the minimum daily requirements of all vitamins.

"Number Three: Our deadly enemy, Warfield the hawk, was sighted yesterday on a neighboring farm. This information was communicated by chicken wire. Be advised to watch for this horrible predator at all times. He has taken too many of us in the past.

"And now, I must end on a note of sadness. It has come to my attention over the barn radio that millions of our kin have been destroyed in California by Newcastle's disease, that deadly virus. We are doing all we can for the survivors through a group of selfless chickens known as the Rhode Island Red Cross in conjunction with a courageous nurse who is not of our species, but deserves a warm round of flapping. I refer, of course, to

Florence Nightingale Nightingale."

They applauded, many clucking in sympathy.

"I, therefore, ask all of you to say a silent prayer, be it the Kaddish for chickens of my faith, or a Requiem by chickens of other faiths." They all bowed their combs and began their spiritual moment of contemplation.

When the great flapping of wings pierced the meditation, they at first believed it to be the dreaded Warfield and some made ready to flee, but Hennie blinked unbelievingly to see that familiar, long-absent russet configuration come tailing down into the barnyard at the head of a formation including, just as incredibly, three other chickens! Before they hit the dust in smooth landings, they regaled the startled flock with a variety of eyepopping spins and loops, and pull-outs that thrilled the hearts of pullets, and there was one instant when Rich Littlechick, remembering Errol Flynn, did a "Dawn Patrol" roll before Jonathan tapped him on the tail and got him back in formation.

"Gottenu!" whispered Hennie Younghen Chicken. "It's Jonathan!" And for a microsecond, time fell away and he could see himself as Jonathan's old buddy, clowning and doing the jokes ("Show me a rooster who

**Our heroes return,
to a curious and admiring flock.**

wakes up the farm and I'll show you an alarm cluck."). But Marilyn, noticing the old youthful gleam, shot him a reproving glance and he grumbled to himself, "Now take my wife—please."

"Fool," she hissed. "Don't you remember that he was driven away by Tevyeh, that he violated the tradition of chickendom and that you as the new leader are sworn to uphold it?"

And so, Hennie, reminded of his status, drew himself up to his full twelve-inch height. With a claw, he traced a long line in the dust and turned to his flock. In a vehement tone, he said "Do not go beyond this line. He and his friends are outcasts. Those who cross this line to communicate with them shall also be considered outcasts. I alone will talk to him." Only one crossed, but this was forgiveable, for it was merely Old Overholt, an ancient rooster whose eyes were so bad he mistook the line for the world's longest worm and tried to suck it up.

Hennie stepped pontifically toward the four fliers, rakish and gallant with their oak-leaf clusters.

"Jonathan, why have you come back to disturb the tranquility of our lives?"

"Hennie," said Jonathan in a choked voice, "I have come back out of love and respect for my kind to point the way to a better life for all chickens. I have traveled far, seen much, and want to share all this . . . ''

But Henny's back was stiffened obdurately, he was walking away, his ears shut to the pleas, and Jonathan felt a profound sorrow that even an old nesting buddy could not overcome the fear of newness.

The others of the flock, also afraid to incur his wrath, paraded behind him, but there were a few cockerels who cast covetous looks at the foursome and Jonathan could perceive a longing to emulate their dash and bravado.

So he wisely took his aerial circus to that nearby meadow and there each day they went through their diamond formations, V-formations, even a T-formation, for the clever Rich Littlechick was also able to mimic Johnny Unitas.

In the passing weeks, despite Hennie's edict, those younger elements were whispering among one another, ''Man, that flying is a gas and they're doing it *without* gas!'' and one by one, in open defiance, they crossed the line, both on the ground and in their minds, and became eager fledglings in an ever-growing armada.

Now Rich Littlechick, slipping into his Peter O'Toole voice and becoming a sort of flying Mr. Chips, had a squadron of his own; so did Woody, who kept his charges amused with his witty patter about his erotic failures in the henhouse, and sexy Ali, who gave them a lot to think about in the air during the day and on the ground at night.

Jonathan oversaw the entire operation and within a few days, the peaceful meadow seemed like an airport. "It won't be long until they put in insurance machines," he remarked to Rich.

And at this point, even the elders, Hennie among them, knew that the inevitable was happening, the trend irreversible, the taste of flying freedom too strong to fight. But the old ones, though envious, still refused to ask for flying lessons for their pride was at stake.

One afternoon, as Jonathan sat talking to thousands of chickens, all rapt at his message, the elders waddled over to the knoll upon which he sat. Hennie interrupted, "Jonathan, I must ask you this. Here you are with thousands of the flock at your feet, entranced by your new way of life. Tell me, do you," and he stammered, "do you think that you are Jesus Christ, Superchicken?"

"Oy vay, no!" Jonathan responded. "That's *trouble!* With a name like Segal, forget it! You remember what happened last time? No, what I teach is purely in my Jewish

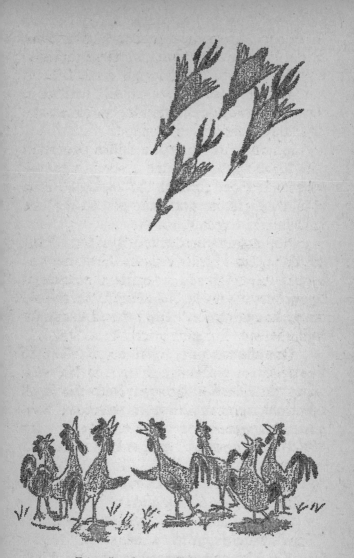

Jonathan's squadron prepares
for Warfield the Hawk.

tradition. Have we not always been seekers of knowledge, questers for truth, advocates of a better life for all creaturekind?"

As he spoke, all listened so intently that they did not notice the dark shape hovering over them; there was a sudden screech and bolting out of the blue came their deadliest foe, Warfield the hawk!

Panic raced through the flock and those who could fly forgot their newly acquired skill and skittered around the meadow, colliding with one another, in terror of the talons.

Warfield's maddened eyes fixated on the fattest, Hennie, and he sunk those horrid talons into the leader's fleshy breast. Hennie squawked pitifully. "Run," he screamed to the others, "run, save yourselves!"

One did not run.

Jonathan Segal Chicken.

"Take me on!" he squawked defiantly at the hawk, who put down the terrorized Hennie to laugh harshly.

"What have we here? A brave chicken? A chicken who isn't?"

In answer, Jonathan took off from the knoll and came zooming toward his archenemy and the battle was joined. A chicken and a hawk were about to commence a dogfight.

To the onlookers, it seemed one-sided. How could Jonathan ever match that hideous array of talons and curved beak? But they had not reckoned with his incredible maneuverability and stout heart.

Again and again, the hawk lunged in for killing rakes across the russet body, only to find that Jonathan had easily slipped by and flown behind him to tickle his tail. And soon all the chickens were laughing in an unrestrained fashion.

Hennie, although badly scratched, reverted to his old comedic form and said, "How do you like that? A chicken is giving a hawk a goose and he's too clumsy to duck." He had put it all together for the best one-liner of his life.

Around and around Jonathan flew, pecking, jabbing, slapping out with a wing until the hawk began to pant with sheer exhaustion and whimpered, "I surrender, I surrender." Jonathan picked up an olive branch from a tree in the Berkowitzes' orchard, shoved it into the beak of his beleaguered, bewildered foe and sent him off limping with a clarion cry, "Never again!"

And his adversary of the aviary gratefully flew away as best he could, beaten and shamed. A hawk had been turned into a dove!

With this episode, all resistance to Jonathan melted. They gathered around him to cheer, to fuss over his feathers and even Hennie, whose wounds happily were superficial, lumbered over to embrace his old pal and crack, "Jonathan, when they made you, they threw away the shell! Okay, teach me to fly."

Thus, serenity reigned at the Berkowitz farm and all were at last united. But Jonathan could not find peace, for were there not other barnyards, other flocks throughout the country, yea verily, the world, where his guidance was needed?

Then one morning, when all was peaceful and every chicken was in one stage of flight or another, Jonathan heard an agonized lowing sound from the barn. It was his four-footed friend, Esther Holstein Cow.

"Oh, what's wrong?" Jonathan asked.

"Don't ask." But she flipped her tail to touch the barn radio nearby. It had been placed there by Farmer Berkowitz because he had read in the Farmers Almanac that music had the charm to make the savage beast produce. In the past, it certainly had. During the Dizzy Gillespie bop era of her youth, one stirring solo from the trumpet star was worth ten gallons. When rock 'n' roll came in, the amplified guitars twanged out another twenty gallons, the Beatles, in particular, giving Esther a "Hard Day's Night."

Bad news from the Middle East.
Jonathan's blood races...

Now in the twilight of her life, she preferred to give to Montovani and his hundred strings. But now, he could see, she was cold with fear, so much so that ice cream was shooting right out of her udders.

"What is it?" Jonathan said again. "What are you shaking for?"

"It's a news bulletin from the Middle East. The Arabs are using the latest Russian planes to attack the Israelis."

"But that's thousands of miles away."

"I don't care how far. If a Holstein shouldn't worry about Israel, who should?"

Her concern cut through the discontent that had lingered in Jonathan, even during his triumphs. Now he knew where his destiny lay, for he was not just a chicken, but a Kosher chicken and he was needed in this moment of crisis.

He gathered the entire flock for a farewell on the meadow and told them he must leave and why.

"But how can we continue without you, Jonathan?" said the elders. "We still have so much to learn. And who will lead us? Poor Hennie is so scarred from that hawk affair, we retired him and put him on Medi-Chick."

"Rich Littlechick will be the new elder. He is wise, fair, intelligent and does a marvelous impression of a president.

112

"I'll miss you, Jonathan," Rich said. "And I'll try to live up to your mandate. But who will be the top flight instructor?"

"Woody," Jonathan said. "And Ali will be the head hen."

All of them, as soon as they were given positions of authority, seemed to mature instantly. "We'll take care of things, don't worry," they promised.

With a last wave of his russet flippers, Jonathan rose, circled the Berkowitz farm and headed into the Eastern sun, a gleaming wraith of a figure in its rays.

Major General Hakkim En Sakkim, the famed "Red Sheik" of the Egyptian Air Force, sat at the controls of his brand-new Russian-supplied Foxbat jet, supremely confident that nothing Israel could send up on this brilliant day over the Suez Canal could match its supersonic speed and mobility. Flying at the apex of a V-formation of five planes, he chattered over his radio to the pilots at his side, "Camel Leader One to all planes. Target nearing. Prepare rockets. Acknowledge."

Camel Drivers One through Four sent back their answering responses and the V tightened, looking in the sky like some loathsome dagger point, ready to be thrust into the very heart of Israel's Knesset, the Parliament. And the Red Sheik chortled for even the U.S.-made Phantoms rising to meet the invaders seemed slow-winged and ludicrously simple to avoid. The Egyptians flew over Sinai, cut north and headed for helpless Jerusalem.

On the top of Mount Scopus, Jonathan, who had paused to rest after his non-stop flight from New York, heard the droning and knew he had arrived not a moment too soon. He saw the V of the Foxbats powering down and wondered, would he have enough strength left to meet this challenge? What could he, a mere chicken, do against this sophisticated technology? But in his mind, The Voice of the Great Chicken said, *"Any creature can do something more than he was born to do."* With new vitality, he rose, his russet body seemingly ablaze with some inner fire. He headed straight for the formation, fixing his eyes upon the goggled face of the Red Sheik, now split by a grin of confidence, but that face quickly changed in amazement.

"By the beard of the Prophet, they're sending up a chicken! I've heard of the wonders the Israelis do with chicken soup, but this is the first time I've ever seen a souped-up chicken. Prepare to launch rockets.

114

... and he's off to Israel,
to do battle over the Suez.

Before he could press the button that would send these lethal missiles into the heart of the Knesset, Jonathan, who had already decided what to, was doing it. Head down, his body a russet blur, flying faster than ever he had before, he became the world's first chickami-kazi, crashing his sinews and bones head-on into the nose of the lead Foxbat. The impact drove it back into the other planes on each flank and in a blinding ball of fire the formation of five planes and one magnificent chicken disintegrated!

And all the searching party found in the Judean Hills were jagged bits of a jet engine, a scorched pair of goggles, some burned fragments of an attack map . . . and a wishbone.

On the ground, the old prime minister of Israel, who had witnessed the miracle, whispered, "Who was that chicken? I . . . I wanted to thank him."

Epilogue

After the blinding flash that had momentarily put him in limbo, Jonathan awoke, surprisingly in no pain, but terribly confused.

Did I survive? he asked himself. Extraordinary fowl that I am, could I have gotten through that head-on crash with a jet thousands of times my weight? And where am I?

"Jonathan Segal Chicken ..." It was The Voice, deep, sonorous, yet tender.

"Who is that?" Jonathan said timorously.

"It is I."

"Oh, my God!"

"You said a beakful."

And Jonathan knew he was in heaven. One glance of his body confirmed this suspicion, for his russet color was gone and in its place shimmering silver. Even his beak was

119

made now of solid gold, his eyes shone like sapphires.

"*Come in, my son,*" and Jonathan flew effortlessly past great cloud banks through an opened door and into a scene of ineffable beauty that would have made Shangri-La look like Levittown. There was a huge hall ten thousand cubits high, its walls ornate with magnificent paintings, its floor strewn with marble statuary, and on each side were choruses of seraphim and cherubim singing hosannas to him.

"Oh, this is superb, beyond belief," exulted Jonathan.

"You ain't seen nothin' yet," said Jolson, popping from behind a pillar and dropping to one knee.

"Come in, come in!" came a chorus of voices and he followed the sound through an archway and there was a banquet table at which sat a galaxy of immortals, Moses, in the stately robe he had worn for his audiences with Pharaoh; Mark Twain, his white suit and hair agleam; Lincoln, his oft-depicted look of sorrow gone and those eyes twinkling with merriment . . . and Socrates, and Aristotle, and Locke, and Madam Curie, Ruth, and Joan of Arc and Rebecca . . . all men and women who had left the earth a better place for having lived there.

"Come in, my son," The Voice said . . .

And they passed him from hand to hand, kissed him, bade him welcome, pressed choice tidbits into his beak of the finest sturgeon, Beluga caviar, pates, gave him sips of Malaga wine and soon the table was rocking to the noise of the celebration.

"Oy," said Moses, "this noise is giving me such a headache!"

"Take two tablets, my son," said The Voice, *"and if that doesn't work, check into Mount Sinai."*

All day the revelry waxed on, singing, dancing, all in his honor, the praise pouring like wine from the golden goblets.

Yes, they praised him, they exalted him, they hugged and embraced him.

And, because it was Friday night, they ate him. For, dear readers, all morals and philosophies aside . . . isn't that just what a Chicken is for?

On the following pages are some
Arrow Books that will be of interest

FOOTBALL DAFT
by Michael Parkinson

Michael Parkinson is football daft.

He caught the disease from his father who stood for forty years in the same spot watching Barnsley F.C., a remarkable feat of endurance hitherto unrecorded.

Michael Parkinson stood alongside his father for sixteen of those years before leaving Barnsley to seek his fortune elsewhere.

He watches for signs of football mania in his three sons. His vigilance was rewarded when, on asking his five year old boy who he most wanted to be when he grew up, he was told 'Bobby Charcoal'.

'The most entertaining sports writer in the country' –
Granada T.V.

'Pathetic' – Liverpool fan

'Mr Parkinson should go far . . . Australia perhaps.'
– Football League official.

CRICKET MAD
by Michael Parkinson

Michael Parkinson was born in a part of Yorkshire where it was perfectly normal to be cricket mad.

Since reaching a mature age and moving down south he has learned to curb his madness. Nowadays he stares out of train windows imagining he is Garfield Sobers rattling up a triple century.

He is not a member of the M.C.C. because he doesn't speak the language and moreover has an irresistible desire to take off his shirt whenever he goes to Lords.

His favourite ground is Bramall Lane, his favourite flower is a white rose and his favourite cricketers are Yorkshiremen. He is renowned throughout cricket for the unbiased flavour of his writing.

THE ART OF COARSE ACTING
by Michael Green

What is a Coarse Actor? He is an actor who can remember his lines but not the order in which they come. An Amateur. One who performs in Church Halls. Often the scenery will fall down. He will usually be playing three parts – Messenger, 2nd Clown, an Attendant Lord.

His aim is to upstage the rest of the cast. His hope is to be dead by Act II so that he can spend the rest of the time in the pub.
His problems?
Everyone else connected with the production.

Michael Green is the author of the best-selling ART OF COARSE RUGBY.

THE ART OF COARSE SPORT
by Michael Green

'Perhaps the only satisfactory definition of a Coarse Sportsman: One who when his club receives a grant from the Playing Fields Association, wants to spend it on extending the bar.' The Coarse Sportsman comes in many shapes – most of them peculiar. He is enthusiastic – except when actually faced with a game. He is healthy – able to spend long hours on his feet in crowded bars. He is unlucky – Acts of God, blind referees or umpires, the Other Side and stray dogs always frustrate his most brilliant feats. He is sporting – always prepared to apologise to the man he has just crippled. Nor is he a coward – just abnormally sensitive to physical pain. He is the backbone of any Game.

THE WORLD OF GOLD TODAY
by Timothy Green

Gold: non-rusting, malleable, ductile, soluble in aqua regia (nitric and hydrochloric acid), molecular weight 197.0, specific density 19.3, melts at 1063° centigrade . . .

Gold, in fact and fiction: the motive and occasion for theft, riot, murder, mayhem, romance and treachery.

Gold is mined, refined, cast, beaten and minted. It is hoarded, traded and smuggled. Gold is sensational news – 'World gold market crisis'.

The world of gold can be dramatic, complicated, mysterious. The workings of the world affect us all.